Can you find
Blaze's flame badge
on every page?

BLAZE AND THE MONSTER MACHINES: SUPER-SPEED ACTIVITY BOOK
A CENTUM BOOK 9781910917084
Published in Great Britain by Centum Books Ltd
This edition published 2016
1 3 5 7 9 10 8 6 4 2

© 2016 Viacom International Inc. All Rights Reserved.

Centum Books Ltd, 20 Devon Square, Newton Abbot, Devon, TQ12 2HR, UK
books@centumbooksltd.co.uk
CENTUM BOOKS Limited Reg. No. 07641486
A CIP catalogue record for this book is available from the British Library
Printed in China.

Centum

Engines ready! **Follow the tyre marks with your finger to race Blaze through Axle City to the Monster Dome.**

SHOUT
'**HIGH TYRE**'
when you get to
the end.

SPEEDY COLOURING

Blaze and his racing partner AJ are ready to roll!
Colour them in with your brightest pens.

Blaze
AJ

TRACE over the dots
to write their names.

LET'S PAINT!

The Monster Machines come in lots of awesome bright colours. **Can you draw lines to match the trucks to their paint?**

COLOUR this paint to match Blaze.

ANSWERS ON PAGE 48

TYRE CHANGE

Hoppin' hubcaps!

How many wheels can you count on this page?

Which racing champ does this **RED WHEEL** belong to?

....

There are .... wheels.

The cowgirl Monster Machine has swung into Gabby's garage. **Help fix Starla by drawing lines to match her parts.**

Where do you go for a **check-up?**

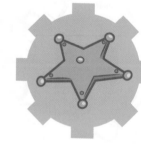

6

ANSWERS ON PAGE 48

COWGIRL CATCH

Yeehaw! One of Starla's lassos has caught Gabby's toolbox. **Which one is it?**

Can you **SPOT** a **spanner** and a **magnet** on this page?

ANSWERS ON PAGE 48

SPOT THE DIFFERENCE

Zeg loves smashing and bashing so much that his picture got jumbled! **Can you spot 5 differences in the second picture?**

Zeg looks like a **Triceratops dinosaur.** What's your favourite dinosaur?

ANSWERS ON PAGE 48

DINO MONSTER TRUCK

Turn your favourite dino into a Monster Machine!
Use your imagination and draw it here.

My Dino Monster Machine is called

....

Gaskets! AJ is ready to race – but where's Blaze? **Help AJ hurry through the maze to find his best pal.**

When you're finished, do a **thumbs-up.** Just like AJ!

ANSWERS ON PAGE 48

COLOUR AJ

Colour the thrill-loving Monster Machine driver so he's ready for blazing speed!

AJ

11

TOOLBOX MATCH

Gabby is the Monster Machine mechanic, and everything she needs is in her trusty toolbox.
Draw lines to connect the matching toolboxes.

One toolbox has **no match**. Which one is it?

ANSWERS ON PAGE 48

SPANNER SUMS

Gabby needs her spanners to tune up the trucks.

Can you help her count them all?

TRACE over your answer.

DOT TO DOT

Blaze can transform into all sorts of vehicles in a flash!
Join the dots to see what he's become this time...

WHAT VEHICLE IS BLAZE?

He's a ....

Mmmmonster Machine!

Now **COLOUR IN** Blaze.

LET'S FIX STRIPES

Growl! Help put Stripes back together so he's ready for action.
Match the missing pieces below.

Stripes is like an animal . . . **but which one?** What can pounce and climb, and is orange with black stripes?

 A

 B

 C

 D

 E

ANSWERS ON PAGE 48

15

The Monster Machines are as BIG as they are *fast!*

Which truck is BIGGEST? Draw a square around him.

Which truck is smallest? **Draw a triangle around him.**

Make the
Monster Dome
by carefully
pressing out the
background and
two supports.

Line up the slits
in the supports
with the slits in
the background,
as shown below,
then push them
into place.

**YOUR BLAZIN'
DOME IS READY
TO STAND!**

MONSTER RAMPS

READY FOR SOME DARING STUNTS?

Press out the ramp pieces and four supports. Slot two supports into each ramp, and stand your ramps in front of the Monster Dome.

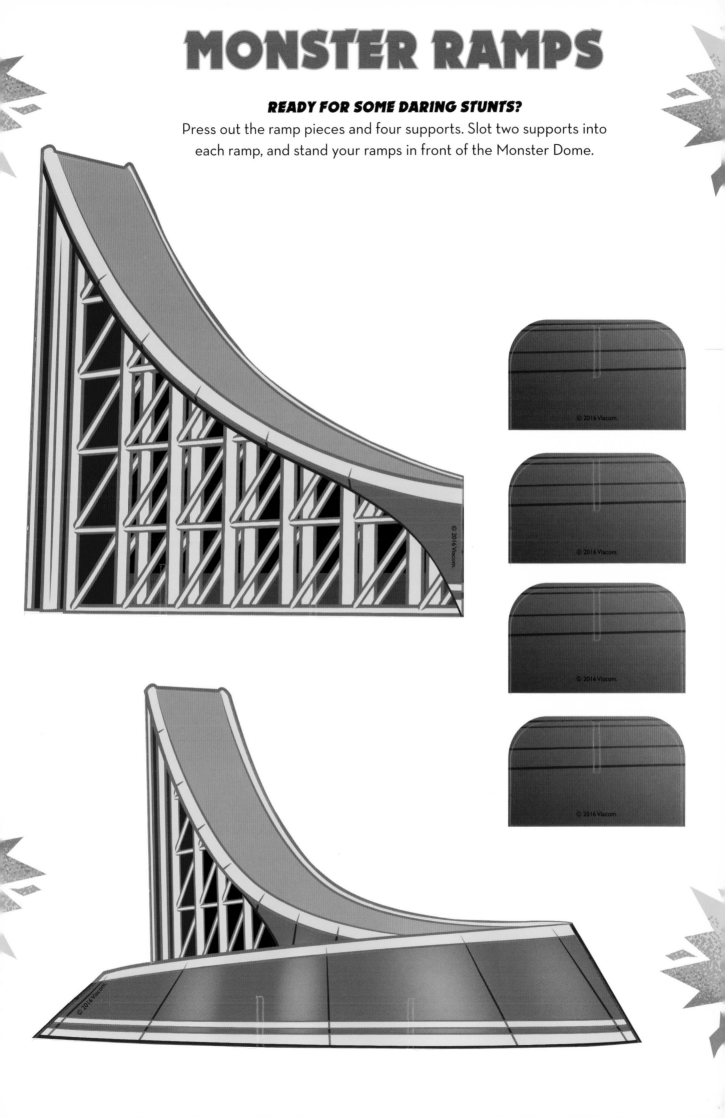

MONSTER MACHINES

Press out all the Monsters Machines and slot each one onto their support.
NOW YOU'RE READY TO ROLL!

© 2016 Viacom.

BLAZE

RACE THE TRUCKS AROUND THE MONSTER DOME AND ZOOM THEM UP THE RAMPS.
HIGH TYRE!

ZEG

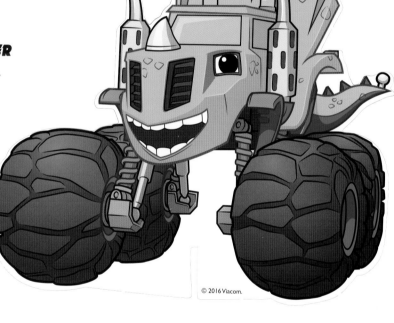

© 2016 Viacom.

© 2016 Viacom.

STARLA

© 2016 Viacom.

DARINGTON

STRIPES

© 2016 Viacom.

© 2016 Viacom.

PICKLE

CRUSHER

IN A PICKLE

Pickle has lost Crusher because he was too busy watching Blaze race. **Help the little sidekick catch up with his friend – before he notices!**

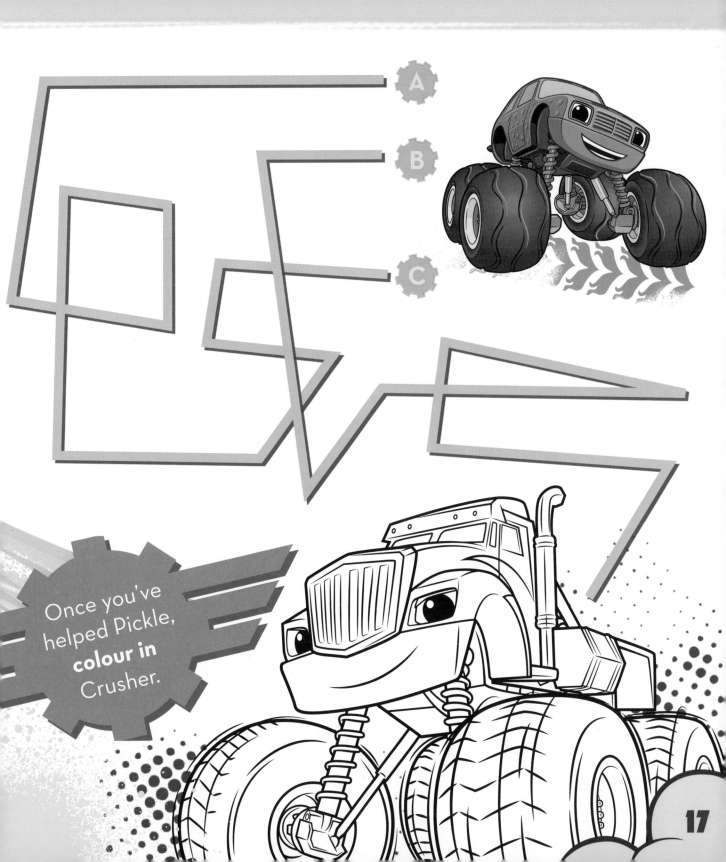

Once you've helped Pickle, **colour in** Crusher.

Every Monster Machine has their own awesome wheel style. **Draw patterns on the trucks' tyres to get them ready to roll!**

Point to your favourite Monster Machine.

19

VISOR VIEW

AJ has switched to his helmet's visor view, but some Monster Machines have got in the way! **Who are they?**

Copy the name of each truck under their picture.

Blaze

Pickle

Starla

Stripes

Crusher

1

....

2

....

3

....

4

....

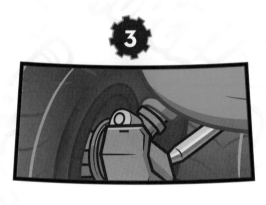

5

....

ANSWERS ON PAGE 48

MONSTER MACHINE MATCH

Oopsie! Only two of these Pickles are exactly the same. **Can you find them?**

Pickle is green. Can you name five other things that are **green?**

ANSWERS ON PAGE 48

21

COLOUR STARLA

Well, bust my bumpers! Starla's in need of an awesome paint job. **Help her out with your colouring pens.**

What **shape** is the badge on Starla's hat?

DARINGTON STUNTS

Darington loves doing tricks and stunts . . .
but he often forgets about the landing!
Which Darington is in one piece?

1

2

3

4

GRAVITY is the force that pulls Darington – and everybody – back to the ground after a jump.

ANSWERS ON PAGE 48

COUNTING TRUCKS

How speedy are your sums? **Add up the trucks and write your answers in the boxes to race to the finish.**

1 [truck] + [truck] + [truck] =

2 [trucks] + [trucks] + [trucks] + [trucks] =

3 [truck] + [truck] =

4 [trucks] + [trucks] + [trucks] + [trucks] + [trucks] + [trucks] =

ADD UP your Blaze and Stripe answers. **What do you get?**

ANSWERS ON PAGE 48

ODD ONE OUT

Well, racing fans . . . **which picture of the daring duo is different to the others?**

Blaze and AJ like to go **FAST.** What's the opposite of fast?

ANSWERS ON PAGE 48

STAR MECHANIC

Gaskets! Blaze needs a repair from his star mechanic, Gabby, but he's far away. **Help her through the maze to the racing hero.**

DISTANCE is the amount of space between two places or things. **Can you guess the opposite of far?**

ANSWERS ON PAGE 48

TYRE MIX-UP

Lugnuts! The Monster Machines' tyres have been mixed up. **Can you match the missing tyres to the right trucks?**

A

B

Can you **guess** which truck this tyre belongs to?

BLAZE

ZEG

STRIPES

C

ANSWERS ON PAGE 48

COLOUR DARINGTON

Add some **dazzling colour** to Darington before he's fired from the cannon!

Darington is blue. Can you name 5 other things that are **blue?**

ANIMAL MONSTER MACHINE

Stripes is an animal monster truck. What's your favourite animal? **Add some big wheels to it and turn it into a Monster Machine!**

This is a _____ Monster Machine.

RACE WITH BLAZE!

Follow the pictures of Blaze with your pen to speed round the racetrack!

Don't bump into the other trucks – especially Crusher!

START

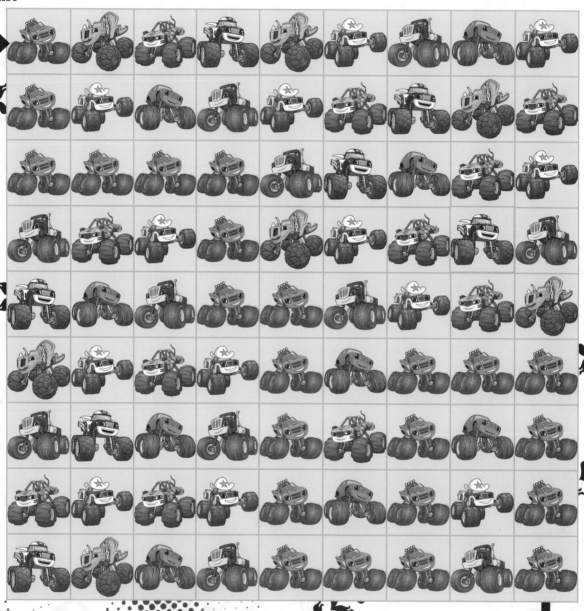

FINISH

How many Crushers can you **COUNT** in the grid?

ANSWERS ON PAGE 48

SHADOW MATCH

Can you match the Monster Machines to their shadows?
Draw lines to pair them up.

1

2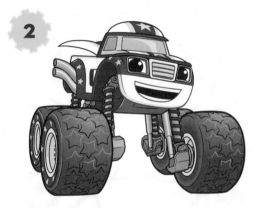

3

4

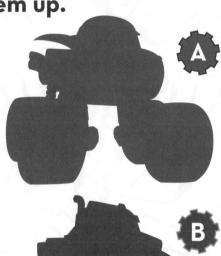
A

B

C

D

Who is the dino truck? Guess the shadow.

DARING STUNTS

Wahooo! Darington has just taken off from a ramp at full speed! But which ramp? **Follow the lines to find out.**

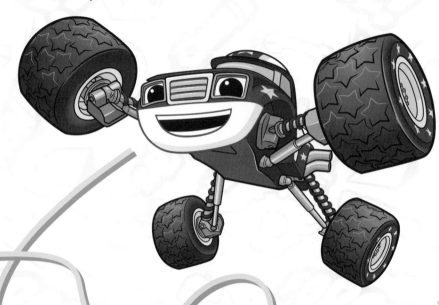

When you get the answer, do your **BIGGEST jump** into the air!

A

B

C

ANSWERS ON PAGE 48

ENGINE ROAR!

What's happened to Stripes? **Complete the clawesome picture of him by drawing his missing parts.**

STRIPES

SPOT CRUSHER

Crusher is one tricky truck! **Only one of these Monster Machines is the real Crusher – can you find him?**

Hint: The real Crusher is different from all the others.

ANSWERS ON PAGE 48

CRUSHING THE COMPETITION

Crusher loves making gadgets . . . to help him cheat! This is his tricky Pineapple Blaster. What else might he fire out of it? **Draw all your ideas flying through the air!**

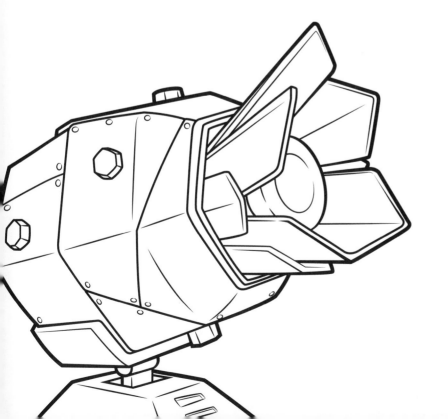

MONSTER MACHINE PATTERNS

Are you in it to win it? See if you can you work out which truck comes next! **Circle your answer each time.**

1

2

3

4

How many times does **Starla** appear on the page?

ANSWERS ON PAGE 48

COLOUR ZEG

This smasher and basher has just had a much-needed wash! **Colour in Zeg to make him just like new.**

Smashing and bashing uses force. **FORCE** is the power used to push or pull something.

ZEG

STARLA'S RANCH

Where do you think Starla lives? **Pick the perfect place for a hootin', hollerin' cowgirl Monster Machine!**

When you pick your answer, **colour in** that frame.

1

2

3

ANSWERS ON PAGE 48

SPOT THE DIFFERENCE

Well, hoppin' hubcaps!
Can you spot a difference in each picture of Starla?

1

2

3

4

5

Trace a star for each difference you find.

ANSWERS ON PAGE 48

SEEING STRIPES!

Stripes can leap and pounce like a cat!
How many tiger trucks can you sniff out on this page?

Leaping is a kind of **MOTION**, like rolling or spinning. What other ways of **moving** can you think of?

I can see .... trucks.

ANSWERS ON PAGE 48

ZEG SMASH!

Which Zeg is the odd one out?
Draw a square around your answer.

What other things start with the letter 'Z'?

ANSWERS ON PAGE 48

CATCH CRUSHER!

Crusher has cheated . . . again! But Blaze has got the drive to catch up! **Which tyre marks should Blaze follow to catch Crusher?**

Blaze needs to accelerate to catch Crusher. You **ACCELERATE** when you start going at a faster speed.

ANSWERS ON PAGE 48

STARLA'S SHAPES

What in tarnation?! **Can you spot all these shapes somewhere on Starla?**

Which other Monster Machine also has a **star shape** on him?

circle

star

rectangle

BLAZE OF GLORY!

Can you spot 5 differences between these pictures of Blaze and AJ? High tyre!

Blaze and AJ are best pals. Who is your **best friend**?

44

ANSWERS ON PAGE 48

ENGINES READY!

Ready to roll? **Trace over the letters to find out what Blaze is saying.**

High tyre!

Now you've written it, **SHOUT IT OUT!**

ANSWERS ON PAGE 48

IN THE MONSTER DOME

A

ANSWERS ON PAGE 48

B

It's time for some crazy stunts! **Look carefully at these pages, and then see if you can spot where the pictures appear in the scene.**

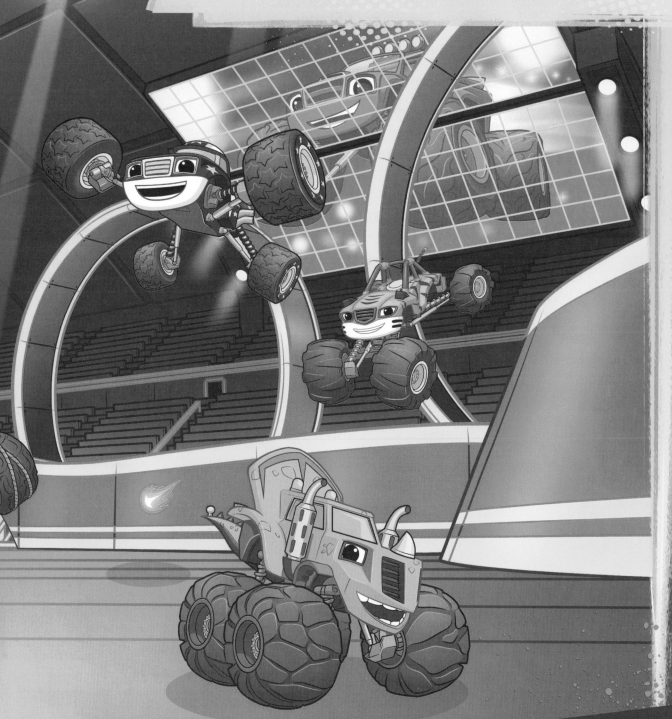

C

D

You're a
**Monster Machine
CHAMPION!**

47

ANSWERS

Did you find all of Blaze's flame badges? Zoom back through the pages to check you didn't miss any!

PAGE 4

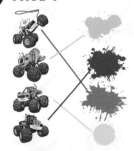

PAGE 5
There are 11 wheels.

The red wheel belongs to Blaze.

PAGE 6

PAGE 7
Lasso B.

PAGE 8

PAGE 10

PAGE 12
A-F; B-E; C-G.
Toolbox D has no match.

PAGE 13
There are 9 spanners.

PAGE 15
1-A; 2-C; 3-B; 4-E; 5-D.
Stripes is like a tiger.

PAGE 17
B.

PAGE 20
1-Crusher; 2-Stripes;
3-Blaze; 4-Starla;
5-Pickle.

PAGE 21
2 and 3.

PAGE 23
3.

PAGE 24
1=3; 2=4; 3=2; 4=5.
Blaze + Stripes = 8.

PAGE 25
3.

PAGE 26

PAGE 27
A-Zeg; B-Stripes; C-Blaze.

The tyre belongs to Starla.

PAGE 30

There are 11 Crushers in the grid.

PAGE 31
1-C; 2-A; 3-D; 4-B.
The shadow is Zeg.

PAGE 32
Ramp B.

PAGE 34
C.

PAGE 36
1- 2-
3- 4-
Starla appears 4 times.

PAGE 38
2.

PAGE 39

PAGE 40
There are 11 trucks.

PAGE 41
4.

PAGE 42
Tyre marks C.

PAGE 43

PAGE 44

PAGE 45
High tyre!

PAGE 46 & 47

48